CW00566922

The SIGN of the FOUR

The **SIGN** *of the* **FOUR**

ADAPTED FROM THE ORIGINAL NOVEL BY

SIR ARTHUR CONAN DOYLE

ILLUSTRATED BY

I.N.J. CULBARD

TEXT ADAPTED BY

IAN EDGINTON

SELF MADE HERO

First published 2010 by SelfMadeHero
139–141 Pancras Road
London NW1 1UN
www.selfmadehero.com

Copyright © 2010 SelfMadeHero
This edition printed in 2017

Adapted by Ian Edginton
Art by I.N.J. Culbard
Layout by Andy Huckle

Publishing Director: Emma Hayley
Sales & Marketing Manager: Sam Humphrey
Editorial & Production Manager: Guillaume Rater
UK Publicist: Paul Smith
US Publicist: Maya Bradford
Designer: Txabi Jones
Textual Consultant: Nick de Somogyi
With thanks to: Catherine Cooke and Jane Laporte

Dedications
For Katy and Joseph and Benjamin – I.N.J. Culbard

*For my son Seth and the trio of lovely ladies in my life: my wife,
Jane, and daughters, Constance and Corinthia* – Ian Edginton

A CIP record for this book is available from the British Library

ISBN 978-1-910593-35-6

10 9 8 7 6 5 4 3 2 1

Printed and bound in Slovenia

FOREWORD

"THERE IS SOMETHING DEVILISH IN THIS, WATSON..."

The Sign of the Four was only the second Sherlock Holmes adventure penned by Arthur Conan Doyle – and, judged as an adventure story alone, it's probably the best. Lengthy flashbacks in Doyle's other long-form Holmes tales necessitate a slowing in pace; the short story form, meanwhile, requires ruthless economy of incident. That's not the case here. The story is every bit as intriguing, perplexing and exciting as its three main literary sources: Wilkie Collins' *The Moonstone*, Poe's *The Murders in the Rue Morgue*, Stevenson's *Treasure Island*. Investigating "The Problem of the Sholtos" (as Doyle's original subtitle had it), Holmes and Watson dash about at a frenetic pace, culminating in a thrilling shoot-out on the River Thames. Unsurprising, therefore, that *The Sign of the Four* ranks just behind the gothic horrors of *The Hound of the Baskervilles* as the second most-filmed Holmes story – as zippily realised in the silent Stoll Picture Productions version of 1923 as in the Granada TV film of 1987, with Jeremy Brett's Holmes in breathless pursuit of John Thaw's especially fine Jonathan Small.

Doyle's supporting characters are translated with no less style in Messrs Edginton and Culbard's graphical retelling. Readers of Mr. Edginton's "steampunk" comic strip *Stickleback*, as serialised in *2000 AD*, will recall the devilish imp "Little Tonga", whose no-less-vile antecedent may be found herein. We are as struck as any Watson by the charms of Mr. Culbard's luminous Mary Morstan, without doubt Doyle's loving pen portrait of his first wife, Louisa. My favourite remains the bizarre, aesthetic Thaddeus Sholto. Fascinatingly, Doyle only came to write this second Holmes adventure after a dinner at the Langham Hotel – his host, the managing editor of *Lippincott's Magazine*, who wished to recruit London's most promising literary lights to author new books for serialisation in a forthcoming English edition. Doyle's fellow guest on that occasion was none other than Oscar Wilde, and it seems certain that the divine Thaddeus was created in the reflection of Doyle's notorious dining companion.

Out of that one dinner, therefore, came not only *The Sign of the Four*, but also Wilde's *The Picture of Dorian Gray*. Unlike that infamous portrait, however, this latest retelling proves that *The Sign of the Four* grows fresher with age.

– Alan Barnes
author, *Sherlock Holmes On Screen*

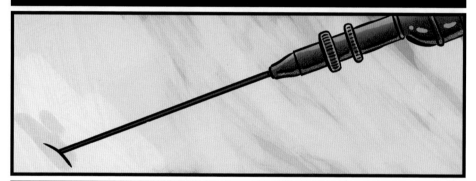

THE CASE IS CONCERNED WITH A WILL AND POSSESSES SOME FEATURES OF INTEREST. HERE IS THE LETTER I HAD THIS MORNING ACKNOWLEDGING MY ASSISTANCE.

HE SEEMS TO SPEAK AS A PUPIL TO HIS MASTER.

OH, HE RATES ME TOO HIGHLY! HE HAS CONSIDERABLE GIFTS HIMSELF IN THE POWERS OF OBSERVATION AND DEDUCTION. HE IS ONLY WANTING IN KNOWLEDGE, AND THAT MAY COME IN TIME.

HE IS CURRENTLY TRANSLATING MY OWN WORKS INTO FRENCH.

YOUR WORKS?

YOU DIDN'T KNOW? I HAVE BEEN GUILTY OF SEVERAL MONOGRAPHS, ALL UPON TECHNICAL SUBJECTS.

RIGHT, ON BOTH POINTS! BUT I CONFESS, I DON'T SEE HOW YOU ARRIVED AT IT. IT WAS A SUDDEN IMPULSE ON MY PART AND I MENTIONED IT TO NO ONE!

IT IS SIMPLICITY ITSELF!

OBSERVATION TELLS ME YOU HAVE A LITTLE REDDISH MOULD ON YOUR INSTEP. NOW, THE PAVEMENT OPPOSITE THE WIGMORE STREET OFFICE HAS BEEN TAKEN UP AND IT IS DIFFICULT TO AVOID TREADING IN THE EXPOSED EARTH...

EARTH OF A PECULIAR REDDISH TINT FOUND ONLY, AS FAR AS I KNOW, IN THAT NEIGHBOUR-HOOD.

AND THE TELEGRAM?

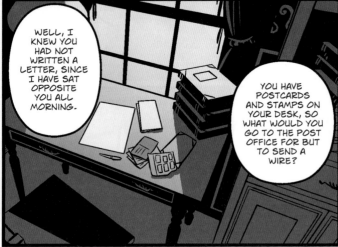

WELL, I KNEW YOU HAD NOT WRITTEN A LETTER, SINCE I HAVE SAT OPPOSITE YOU ALL MORNING.

YOU HAVE POSTCARDS AND STAMPS ON YOUR DESK, SO WHAT WOULD YOU GO TO THE POST OFFICE FOR BUT TO SEND A WIRE?

YOU'RE RIGHT. IT WAS INDEED CLEANED BEFORE BEING SENT TO ME.

I DO JUDGE, HOWEVER, THAT THE WATCH BELONGED TO YOUR ELDER BROTHER, WHO INHERITED IT FROM YOUR FATHER.

THAT YOU NO DOUBT GATHERED FROM THE "H.W." ON THE BACK?

QUITE SO. THE "W." SUGGESTS YOUR OWN SURNAME. THE WATCH IS NEARLY FIFTY YEARS OLD, AS ARE THE ENGRAVED INITIALS. SINCE JEWELLERY USUALLY DESCENDS TO THE ELDEST SON, HE MOST LIKELY HAS THE SAME NAME AS YOUR FATHER.

YOUR FATHER, IF I REMEMBER RIGHTLY, HAS BEEN DEAD MANY YEARS. IT HAS THEREFORE BEEN IN THE HANDS OF YOUR ELDEST BROTHER.

ALL CORRECT, SO FAR. ANYTHING ELSE?

ONLY THAT HE WAS A CARELESS MAN OF UNTIDY HABITS. HE WAS LEFT WITH GOOD PROSPECTS BUT THREW AWAY HIS CHANCES...

HE LIVED IN POVERTY FOR SOME TIME WITH OCCASIONAL INTERVALS OF PROSPERITY UNTIL FINALLY, TAKING TO DRINK, HE DIED.

THAT IS ALL I CAN GATHER.

THIS... THIS IS UNWORTHY OF YOU, HOLMES! I CANNOT BELIEVE THAT YOU'VE DESCENDED TO THIS! YOU HAVE CLEARLY MADE INQUIRIES INTO THE HISTORY OF MY UNHAPPY BROTHER AND NOW PRETEND TO DEDUCE THE KNOWLEDGE IN SOME FANCIFUL WAY!

YOU CANNOT EXPECT ME TO BELIEVE THAT YOU READ ALL THIS FROM THIS OLD WATCH! IT IS UNKIND AND... TO SPEAK PLAINLY, HAS A TOUCH OF THE CHARLATAN ABOUT IT!

MY DEAR DOCTOR, PRAY ACCEPT MY APOLOGIES!

IT'S AS CLEAR AS DAYLIGHT NOW. I REGRET THE INJUSTICE I DID YOU. I SHOULD HAVE HAD MORE FAITH IN YOUR MARVELLOUS FACULTY.

MAY I ASK WHETHER YOU'RE ENGAGED IN ANY PROFESSIONAL INQUIRIES AT PRESENT?

NONE. HENCE THE COCAINE. I CANNOT LIVE WITHOUT BRAINWORK. WHAT IS THE USE OF HAVING POWERS, DOCTOR, WHEN ONE HAS NO FIELD UPON WHICH TO EXERT THEM?

I...

KNOCK! KNOCK!

MRS. HUDSON?

A YOUNG LADY IS HERE TO SEE YOU, MR. HOLMES.

MISS MARY MORSTAN

I BELIEVE YOU CANNOT SAY THE SAME OF MINE. MR. HOLMES, I CAN HARDLY IMAGINE ANYTHING MORE STRANGE, MORE UTTERLY INEXPLICABLE THAN THE SITUATION I FIND MYSELF IN.

YOU WILL WISH TO TALK PRIVATELY. SO, IF YOU WILL EXCUSE ME...

PLEASE, MR. HOLMES. IF YOUR FRIEND WOULD BE GOOD ENOUGH TO STOP, HE MIGHT BE OF INESTIMABLE SERVICE TO ME!

BY ALL MEANS.

BRIEFLY, GENTLEMEN, THE FACTS ARE THESE...

"MY FATHER WAS AN OFFICER IN AN INDIAN REGIMENT. MY MOTHER DIED WHEN I WAS A CHILD AND I WAS SENT HOME TO ENGLAND."

"HAVING NO RELATIVE HERE, I WAS PLACED IN A COMFORTABLE BOARDING ESTABLISHMENT IN EDINBURGH, WHERE I REMAINED UNTIL I WAS SEVENTEEN."

"IN 1878, MY FATHER OBTAINED TWELVE MONTHS' LEAVE AND CAME HOME. HE TELEGRAPHED ME TO COME DOWN AND MEET HIM IN LONDON, AT THE LANGHAM HOTEL."

HIS LUGGAGE?

REMAINED AT THE HOTEL. THERE WAS NOTHING IN IT TO SUGGEST A CLUE — SOME CLOTHES, BOOKS AND A CONSIDERABLE NUMBER OF CURIOSITIES FROM THE ANDAMAN ISLANDS.

HE HAD BEEN ONE OF THE OFFICERS IN CHARGE OF THE CONVICT GUARD THERE.

HAD HE ANY FRIENDS IN TOWN?

ONLY ONE THAT WE KNOW OF — MAJOR SHOLTO, OF HIS OWN REGIMENT, THE 34TH BOMBAY INFANTRY.

THE MAJOR HAD RETIRED SOME TIME BEFORE AND LIVED IN UPPER NORWOOD. WE COMMUNICATED WITH HIM, OF COURSE, BUT HE DIDN'T EVEN KNOW HIS BROTHER OFFICER WAS IN ENGLAND.

THIS IS A SINGULAR CASE!

INDEED, BUT I HAVE NOT YET DESCRIBED TO YOU THE MOST SINGULAR PART!

SIX YEARS AGO — THE FOURTH OF MAY, 1882, TO BE EXACT, AN ADVERTISEMENT APPEARED IN *THE TIMES* ASKING FOR THE ADDRESS OF MISS MARY MORSTAN AND STATING IT WOULD BE TO HER ADVANTAGE TO COME FORWARD.

THERE WAS NO NAME OR ADDRESS APPENDED.

"I HAD JUST ENTERED THE FAMILY OF MRS. FORRESTER IN THE CAPACITY OF GOVERNESS. BY HER ADVICE, I PUBLISHED MY ADDRESS IN THE ADVERTISEMENT COLUMN."

"LATER THE SAME DAY, THERE ARRIVED BY POST A SMALL BOX ADDRESSED TO ME, CONTAINING A LARGE, LUSTROUS PEARL."

"NO WORD OF WRITING WAS ENCLOSED."

SINCE THEN, EVERY YEAR, ON THE SAME DATE, THERE ALWAYS APPEARED A SIMILAR BOX, CONTAINING A PEARL, WITHOUT ANY CLUE AS TO THE SENDER...

THEY HAVE BEEN PRONOUNCED BY AN EXPERT TO BE OF A RARE VARIETY AND OF CONSIDERABLE VALUE.

YOU CAN SEE FOR YOURSELF, THEY ARE VERY HANDSOME.

HAS ANYTHING ELSE HAPPENED RECENTLY?

YES, I RECEIVED THIS LETTER THIS MORNING.

POST-MARK LONDON S.W. DATED SEPTEMBER 7TH. THUMB-MARK, POSTMAN'S NO DOUBT. BEST QUALITY PAPER. ENVELOPES AT SIXPENCE A PACKET. A PARTICULAR MAN IN HIS STATIONERY. NO ADDRESS.

IS SHE? I DIDN'T NOTICE.

YOU REALLY ARE AN AUTOMATON! THERE IS SOMETHING POSITIVELY INHUMAN IN YOU AT TIMES!

IT IS OF THE FIRST IMPORTANCE NOT TO ALLOW YOUR JUDGMENT TO BE BIASED BY PERSONAL QUALITIES.

THE MOST WINNING WOMAN I EVER KNEW WAS HANGED FOR POISONING THREE CHILDREN FOR THEIR INSURANCE MONEY...

AND THE MOST REPELLANT MAN OF MY ACQUAINTANCE HAS SPENT NEARLY A QUARTER OF A MILLION POUNDS ON THE LONDON POOR.

YES, BUT IN THIS CASE...

I NEVER MAKE EXCEPTIONS. HERE, WHAT DO YOU MAKE OF THIS FELLOW'S SCRIBBLE?

LEGIBLE AND REGULAR. A MAN OF BUSINESS HABITS AND SOME FORCE OF CHARACTER.

IN QUEST OF A SOLUTION

CAPTAIN MORSTAN DISAPPEARS. THE ONLY PERSON IN LONDON HE COULD HAVE VISITED IS MAJOR SHOLTO, WHO DENIED HAVING HEARD HE WAS IN LONDON.

FOUR YEARS LATER, SHOLTO DIES.

WITHIN A WEEK OF HIS DEATH, MISS MORSTAN RECEIVES A VALUABLE PRESENT, DELIVERED ANNUALLY, CULMINATING IN A LETTER DESCRIBING HER AS A WRONGED WOMAN.

WHAT WRONG CAN IT REFER TO EXCEPT THE LOSS OF HER FATHER! WHY DO THE PRESENTS BEGIN AFTER SHOLTO'S DEATH, UNLESS HIS HEIR KNOWS SOMETHING OF THE MYSTERY AND DESIRES TO MAKE COMPENSATION!

HAVE YOU ANY ALTERNATIVE THEORY WHICH WILL MEET THE FACTS?

BUT WHAT A STRANGE COMPENSATION... AND STRANGELY MADE! WHY WRITE THE LETTER NOW AND NOT SIX YEARS AGO?

IT SPEAKS OF JUSTICE, BUT WHAT JUSTICE IS THERE, BARRING MISS MORSTAN'S FATHER STILL BEING ALIVE?

I TRUST YOU HAVE NO OBJECTION TO TOBACCO SMOKE?

THE BALSAMIC ODOUR OF EASTERN TOBACCO?

I AM A LITTLE... NERVOUS, AND FIND MY HOOKAH AN INVALUABLE SEDATIVE.

MMPH- MMPUH, MMMPH-

MR. SHOLTO, I AM HERE AT YOUR REQUEST TO LEARN SOME- THING YOU WISHED TO TELL ME.

IT IS LATE AND I SHOULD DESIRE THIS INTERVIEW TO BE AS SHORT AS POSSIBLE!

OH, AT BEST IT MAY TAKE SOME TIME. WE SHALL CERTAINLY HAVE TO GO TO NORWOOD TO SEE BROTHER BARTHOLOMEW. HE IS VERY ANGRY WITH ME FOR MY TAKING THE COURSE I HAVE.

YOU CANNOT IMAGINE WHAT A TERRIBLE FELLOW HE IS WHEN HE IS ANGRY.

IF WE ARE TO GO TO NORWOOD, IT WOULD PERHAPS BE AS WELL TO START AT ONCE.

HM? HEH, HEH! OH, NO... THAT WOULD HARDLY DO. HE WOULD NOT TAKE KINDLY TO THAT.

FIRST I MUST LAY THE FACTS BEFORE YOU AS I KNOW THEM.

AS YOU MAY KNOW, MY FATHER WAS MAJOR JOHN SHOLTO, LATE OF THE INDIAN ARMY.

THERE HE PROSPERED, ACCRUING CONSIDERABLE WEALTH, A LARGE COLLECTION OF VALUABLE CURIOSITIES AND A STAFF OF NATIVE SERVANTS.

"ELEVEN YEARS AGO, HE RETIRED TO PONDICHERRY LODGE IN UPPER NORWOOD AND LIVED IN GREAT LUXURY. MY TWIN BROTHER AND I ARE HIS ONLY CHILDREN."

"HOWEVER, SOME MYSTERY OVERHUNG OUR FATHER. HE WAS FEARFUL OF GOING OUT ALONE AND EMPLOYED TWO PRIZE-FIGHTERS TO ACT AS PORTERS AT THE LODGE. WILLIAMS, WHO DROVE YOU HERE TONIGHT, WAS ONE OF THEM."

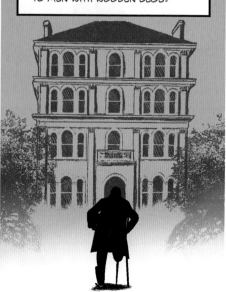

"HE ALSO HAD A MARKED AVERSION TO MEN WITH WOODEN LEGS."

"ON ONE OCCASION, HE ACTUALLY SHOT AT A WOODEN-LEGGED TRADES-MAN WHO WAS HARMLESSLY CANVASSING FOR ORDERS."

"WE HAD TO PAY A LARGE SUM TO HUSH THE MATTER UP."

"EARLY IN 1882, HE RECEIVED A LETTER WHICH WAS OBVIOUSLY A GREAT SHOCK TO HIM, AS FROM THAT DAY HE SICKENED TO HIS DEATH."

"BY THE END OF APRIL, WE WERE INFORMED THAT HE WAS BEYOND HOPE AND WISHED TO MAKE HIS LAST COMMUNICATION WITH US."

"HE MADE A REMARKABLE STATEMENT, HIS VOICE BROKEN AS MUCH BY EMOTION AS BY PAIN."

"I SHALL TRY TO GIVE IT TO YOU IN HIS OWN VERY WORDS..."

IN INDIA, ARTHUR MORSTAN AND I, THROUGH A REMARKABLE CHAIN OF CIRCUMSTANCES, CAME INTO POSSESSION OF A CONSIDERABLE TREASURE...

I BROUGHT IT OVER TO ENGLAND, AND ON THE NIGHT OF MORSTAN'S ARRIVAL, HE CAME TO CLAIM HIS SHARE.

"WE HAD HEATED WORDS REGARDING THE DIVISION OF THE TREASURE..."

"SUDDENLY HIS FACE TURNED A DUSKY HUE AND HE FELL BACKWARDS, CUTTING HIS HEAD ON THE TREASURE-CHEST. TO MY HORROR, HE WAS DEAD."

"HE SUFFERED FROM A WEAK HEART BUT TOLD NO ONE. ONLY I KNEW THIS."

"HIS DEATH AT THE MOMENT OF A QUARREL, AND THE GASH IN HIS HEAD, WOULD LOOK BAD FOR ME. AN OFFICIAL INQUIRY WOULD BE MADE, NO DOUBT BRINGING OUT SOME FACTS ABOUT THE TREASURE."

"I THEN SAW MY SERVANT, LAL CHOWDAR, IN THE DOORWAY. HE THOUGHT I HAD KILLED MORSTAN."

"IF MY OWN SERVANT COULD NOT BELIEVE MY INNOCENCE, HOW COULD I HOPE TO CONVINCE TWELVE FOOLISH TRADESMEN IN A JURY-BOX?"

WE COULD JUDGE THE SPLENDOUR OF THE MISSING RICHES BY THE CHAPLET FATHER HAD TAKEN OUT.

IT WAS ALL I COULD DO TO PERSUADE BARTHOLOMEW TO LET ME FIND OUT MISS MORSTAN'S ADDRESS AND SEND HER A PEARL, DETACHED FROM IT, EVERY YEAR, SO SHE MIGHT NEVER FEEL DESTITUTE.

IT WAS A KINDLY THOUGHT. IT WAS EXTREMELY GOOD OF YOU.

WE WERE YOUR TRUSTEES — THAT WAS THE VIEW I TOOK, THOUGH BROTHER BARTHOLOMEW COULD NOT SEE IT IN THAT LIGHT.

WE HAD PLENTY OF MONEY OUR-SELVES.

BESIDES, IT WOULD HAVE BEEN SUCH BAD TASTE TO HAVE TREATED A YOUNG LADY IN SUCH A... SCURVY FASHION.

YESTERDAY, HOWEVER, I LEARNED THAT AN EVENT OF EXTREME IMPORTANCE HAS OCCURRED... THE TREASURE HAS BEEN DISCOVERED.

I INSTANTLY COMMUNICATED WITH MISS MORSTAN, AND IT ONLY REMAINS FOR US TO DRIVE TO UPPER NORWOOD AND DEMAND OUR SHARE!

THE TRAGEDY OF PONDICHERRY LODGE

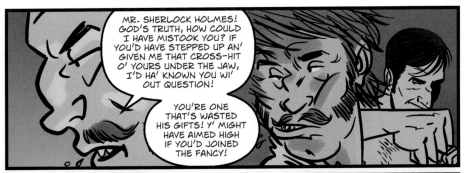

I'M RELIEVED MISS MORSTAN REMAINED DOWNSTAIRS TO COMFORT THE HOUSEKEEPER. SHE HAS ENDURED MUCH ALREADY AND SHOULD NOT WITNESS THIS.

YOU SEE, WATSON!

"THE SIGN OF THE FOUR"! IN GOD'S NAME, WHAT DOES IT MEAN?

IT MEANS MURDER. AH, LOOK HERE!

IT LOOKS LIKE... A THORN?

IT IS. YOU MAY PICK IT UP — BUT BE CAREFUL, IT'S POISONED!

THIS IS ALL AN INSOLUBLE MYSTERY TO ME.

IT GROWS DARKER INSTEAD OF CLEARER.

ON THE CONTRARY! I ONLY REQUIRE A FEW MISSING LINKS TO HAVE AN ENTIRELY CONNECTED CASE!

SHERLOCK HOLMES GIVES A DEMONSTRATION

MUCH HAS HAPPENED SINCE YOU LEFT, WATSON. ATHELNEY JONES HAS ARRESTED THE GATE-KEEPER, THE HOUSE-KEEPER AND THE INDIAN SERVANT. FORTUNATELY, IT MEANT I HAD THE RUN OF THE PLACE, WHICH I PUT TO GOOD USE.

I WENT BACK INTO THE GARRET AND ONTO THE ROOF.

TILES HAD BEEN LOOSENED THE WHOLE WAY, INDICATING THE PATH OF THE MYSTERIOUS ALLY.

IN HIS HASTE, HOWEVER, HE DROPPED THIS.

DON'T PRICK YOURSELF. THEY ARE HELLISH THINGS, BUT I'M DELIGHTED TO HAVE THEM NONE-THELESS, FOR THE CHANCES ARE THEY'RE ALL HE HAS.

THERE'S THE LESS FEAR OF US FINDING ONE IN OUR SKIN BEFORE LONG. I'D SOONER FACE A MARTINI BULLET MYSELF.

ARE YOU GAME FOR A TRUDGE? WILL YOUR LEG STAND IT?

CERTAINLY.

HERE, TOBY, SMELL IT. SMELL IT.

CREOSOTE... FROM THE CARBOY?

INDEED.

I MARVEL AT THE MEANS BY WHICH YOU'VE OBTAINED RESULTS IN THIS CASE, HOLMES, BUT HOW COULD YOU DESCRIBE WITH SUCH CONFIDENCE THE WOODEN-LEGGED MAN?

I DON'T WISH TO BE THEATRICAL, BUT IT WAS SIMPLICITY ITSELF!

TWO OFFICERS, IN COMMAND OF A CONVICT GUARD, LEARN OF A BURIED TREASURE. A MAP IS DRAWN FOR THEM BY AN ENGLISHMAN — JONATHAN SMALL.

YOU'LL RECALL CAPTAIN MORSTAN'S CHART? SMALL SIGNED IT ON BEHALF OF HIMSELF AND HIS ASSOCIATES — "THE SIGN OF THE FOUR".

USING THE CHART, ONE OF THE OFFICERS FINDS THE TREASURE AND BRINGS IT TO ENGLAND, LEAVING SOME CONDITION UNDER WHICH HE RECEIVED IT UNFULFILLED.

WHY NOT SMALL HIM-SELF?

BECAUSE SMALL AND HIS ASSOCIATES ARE THEMSELVES CONVICTS AND HENCE COULD NOT GET AWAY!

MAJOR SHOLTO REMAINS AT PEACE FOR SOME YEARS, HAPPY IN THE POSSESSION OF HIS BOUNTY, UNTIL HE RECEIVES A LETTER FROM INDIA WHICH UNNERVES HIM GREATLY!

IT SAID THE MEN HE'D WRONGED HAD BEEN SET FREE!

ESCAPED, MORE LIKE! SHOLTO GUARDS HIMSELF AGAINST A WOODEN-LEGGED MAN — A WHITE MAN, MARK YOU, FOR HE SHOOTS AT A WHITE TRADESMAN, MISTAKING HIM FOR SMALL.

THE OTHER SIGNATORIES ON THE CHART ARE HINDOOS OR MOHAMMEDANS. THEREFORE WE MAY SAY THAT THE WOODEN-LEGGED MAN IS JONATHAN SMALL.

DOES THE REASONING STRIKE YOU AS BEING FAULTY?

BY NO MEANS. IT IS CLEAR AND CONCISE.

NOW, LET US IMAGINE WE ARE JONATHAN SMALL. HE COMES TO ENGLAND, RESOLVED TO REGAIN WHAT IS HIS AND REVENGE HIMSELF UPON THE MAN WHO HAD WRONGED HIM.

SUDDENLY, HOWEVER, HE LEARNS THE MAJOR IS ON HIS DEATHBED. LEST THE SECRET OF THE TREASURE DIE WITH HIM, SMALL RUNS THE GAUNTLET OF THE GUARDS, AND APPROACHES THE DYING MAN'S WINDOW.

DETERRED BY THE PRESENCE OF SHOLTO'S SONS, HE RETURNS LATER AND SEARCHES THE DEAD MAN'S PAPERS FOR SOME MENTION OF THE HOARD. MAD WITH HATE, HE LEAVES THE INSCRIBED CARD.

HE'D DOUBTLESS PLANNED BEFOREHAND TO SLAY THE MAJOR, AND LEAVE IT AS A RECORD UPON THE BODY — AS A SIGN TO SHOW IT WAS NOT A COMMON MURDER BUT AN ACT OF JUSTICE.

SMALL CAN DO NOTHING BUT KEEP A WATCH ON THE EFFORTS TO FIND THE TREASURE. HE POSSIBLY LEAVES ENGLAND, RETURNING WHEN INFORMED OF THE DISCOVERY IN THE GARRET.

WITH HIS WOODEN LEG, HE'S UNABLE TO REACH THE LOFTY ROOM. HIS CURIOUS ASSOCIATE, HOWEVER, GETS OVER THIS DIFFICULTY BUT DIPS HIS NAKED FOOT INTO THE CREOSOTE...

WHENCE COME TOBY, AND A SIX-MILE LIMP FOR A HALF-PAY OFFICER WITH A DAMAGED TENDO ACHILLIS!

BUT IT WAS THE ASSOCIATE, NOT SMALL, WHO COMMITTED THE CRIME.

QUITE SO — MUCH TO SMALL'S DISGUST, BY THE WAY HE STAMPED AROUND WHEN HE REACHED THE ROOM.

HE BORE NO GRUDGE AGAINST BARTHOLOMEW SHOLTO, BUT THE SAVAGE INSTINCTS OF HIS COMPANION HAD BROKEN OUT.

SMALL THEN LEFT HIS RECORD, LOWERED THE TREASURE-BOX TO THE GROUND AND FOLLOWED IT HIMSELF. THAT IS THE TRAIN OF EVENTS AS FAR AS I CAN DECIPHER THEM.

THE BAKER STREET IRREGULARS

DO YOU RECALL THE BAKER STREET DIVISION OF THE POLICE FORCE I EMPLOYED IN THE JEFFERSON HOPE CASE?

OH, YES!

THIS IS SUCH A CASE WHERE THEY MIGHT BE INVALUABLE. I'LL WIRE MY DIRTY LIEUTENANT, WIGGINS...

"I EXPECT HE AND HIS GANG WILL BE WITH US BEFORE WE HAVE FINISHED OUR BREAKFAST."

GOT YOUR MESSAGE, SIR! BROUGHT 'EM ALL ON SHARPISH!

SO I SEE. IN FUTURE, THEY CAN REPORT TO YOU AND YOU TO ME. I CANNOT HAVE THE HOUSE INVADED LIKE THIS. HOWEVER, AS YOU ARE ALL HERE...

I WISH TO KNOW THE WHERE-ABOUTS OF THE STEAM LAUNCH AURORA, OWNER MORDECAI SMITH. SHE'S BLACK WITH TWO RED STREAKS, FUNNEL BLACK WITH ONE WHITE BAND.

SHE'S DOWNRIVER SOMEWHERE, BUT ALSO KEEP WATCH ON SMITH'S LANDING-STAGE OPPOSITE MILLBANK SHOULD THE BOAT RETURN.

LATER.

YOU KNOW MY THEORY ABOUT THIS NORWOOD CASE, DR. WATSON...

I REMEMBER YOU EXPRESSED ONE, YES.

WELL, I'VE BEEN OBLIGED TO RECONSIDER IT. I HAD MY NET DRAWN TIGHTLY AROUND MR. SHOLTO WHEN HE PROVED TO HAVE AN ALIBI THAT COULDN'T BE SHAKEN!

IT'S A VERY DARK CASE AND MY PROFESSIONAL CREDIT IS AT STAKE. I SHOULD BE VERY GLAD OF A LITTLE ASSISTANCE.

YOUR FRIEND MR. SHERLOCK HOLMES IS A WONDERFUL MAN, WHO'S NOT TO BE BEAT.

WELL, YOU MAY BE IN FOR A LONG WAIT. I CANNOT BE SURE WHEN HE'LL BE BACK.

I DON'T THINK SO. I HAD A WIRE FROM HIM THIS AFTERNOON...

"GO TO BAKER STREET AT ONCE. IF I HAVE NOT RETURNED, WAIT FOR ME. I AM CLOSE ON THE TRACK OF THE SHOLTO GANG. YOU CAN COME WITH US TONIGHT IF YOU WANT TO BE IN AT THE FINISH."

THE END OF THE ISLANDER

I COULD ONLY THINK OF ONE WAY... BY HANDING THE *AURORA* TO SOME BOAT-BUILDER OR REPAIRER TO MAKE A TRIFLING CHANGE TO HER.

SHE WOULD BE REMOVED, CONCEALED IN A SHED OR YARD, YET AVAILABLE AT BUT A FEW HOURS' NOTICE.

"IN MY SEAMAN'S RIG, I ENQUIRED AT ALL THE YARDS DOWN THE RIVER. I DREW A BLANK AT FIFTEEN, BUT AT THE SIXTEENTH — JACOBSON'S — I LEARNED THE *AURORA* HAD BEEN HANDED OVER TWO DAYS AGO BY A WOODEN-LEGGED MAN FOR SOME TRIVIAL REPAIR TO HER RUDDER."

"JUST THEN, THE MISSING OWNER APPEARED. MORDECAI SMITH, MUCH THE WORSE FOR LIQUOR. HE DEMANDED THE LAUNCH BE MADE READY AT EIGHT O'CLOCK SHARP, FOR HE'D TWO GENTLEMEN WHO WEREN'T TO BE KEPT WAITING."

HE'D EVIDENTLY BEEN PAID WELL, FOR HE WAS FLUSH WITH MONEY. I HAD ONE OF THE IRREGULARS STAND SENTRY OVER THE LAUNCH.

THE GREAT AGRA TREASURE

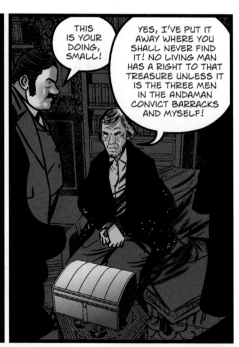

I'M A WORCESTERSHIRE MAN, BORN NEAR PERSHORE. MY FAMILY WERE ALL STEADY, CHAPEL-GOING FOLK, WELL KNOWN AND RESPECTED, WHILE I WAS... A BIT OF A ROVER.

I GOT INTO A MESS OVER A GIRL AND ONLY GOT OUT OF IT BY TAKING THE QUEEN'S SHILLING. I WAS POSTED TO INDIA WITH THE THIRD BUFFS.

A CROCODILE NIPPED THIS OFF WHEN I WAS SWIMMING IN THE GANGES. I WAS FIVE MONTHS IN THE HOSPITAL BEFORE GETTING MY DISCHARGE.

SO, THERE I WAS, A CRIPPLE AT TWENTY, UNFIT FOR ANY ACTIVE OCCUPATION...

"EVEN SO, I FOUND MYSELF A JOB AS AN OVERSEER ON AN INDIGO FARM. I WAS ON HORSEBACK ALL DAY, SO THAT WAS FINE."

"BUT I WAS NEVER IN LUCK FOR LONG. WITHOUT A NOTE OF WARNING, THE GREAT MUTINY WAS ON US. MY MASTER AND HIS FAMILY WERE MURDERED."

"I DIDN'T WAIT. THAT SAME EVENING, I WAS WITHIN THE WALLS AT AGRA, WHICH WAS STILL HELD BY THE BRITISH."

"THE GREAT CITY OF AGRA... IT'S A QUEER PLACE. VAST, FULL OF GREAT HALLS, WINDING PASSAGES AND CORRIDORS."

"BECAUSE I WAS AN EX-SOLDIER AND BRITISH, I WAS PUT IN CHARGE OF ONE OF THE MANY GATES. A COUPLE OF SIKHS STILL LOYAL TO US WERE PUT UNDER MY COMMAND."

"MY TWO PUNJABEES WERE TALL, FIERCE, FIGHTING MEN — MAHOMET SINGH AND ABDULLAH KHAN."

"IT WAS THE THIRD NIGHT OF MY WATCH, AND DREARY WORK, STANDING HOUR AFTER HOUR, BUT THAT WAS SOON TO PROVE THE LEAST OF IT..."

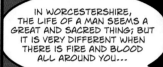

IN WORCESTERSHIRE, THE LIFE OF A MAN SEEMS A GREAT AND SACRED THING; BUT IT IS VERY DIFFERENT WHEN THERE IS FIRE AND BLOOD ALL AROUND YOU...

ONE OF THE LOCAL RAJAHS... HE'D GONE IN WITH THE REBELS, BUT HE'D WANTED TO HEDGE HIS BET, IN CASE THE BRITISH SHOULD COME OUT ON TOP.

"SO HE PLOTTED TO GET HALF HIS TREASURE HIDDEN IN THE FORT OF AGRA, SENDING ONE OF HIS MEN WITH IT DISGUISED AS A MERCHANT AND DOST AKBAR, KHAN'S BROTHER, AS HIS GUIDE."

WHO GOES THERE?

FRIENDS, SAHIB. FRIENDS.

WHAT HAVE YOU WITH YOU?

AN OLD BOX. IT CONTAINS SOME FAMILY PAPERS – UNIMPORTANT, BUT I WOULD NOT LIKE TO LOSE THEM.

PLEASE, SAHIB, I AM NOT A BEGGAR.

YOU WILL BE REWARDED, AND THE GOVERNOR ALSO, IF YOU WILL GIVE ME SHELTER.

IT WAS ALL VERY BAD, BUT IF HE'D ESCAPED THE WHOLE BUSINESS WOULD'VE COME OUT. I'D HAVE BEEN SHOT, MOST LIKE. WHAT WOULD YOU HAVE DONE IN MY PLACE?

GO ON.

"WE BURIED HIM IN A SINKHOLE AND COVERED HIM WITH LOOSE BRICKS. THEN WE TURNED TO THE BOX AND THE TREASURE..."

"IT WAS BLINDING TO LOOK UPON. THERE WERE NINETY-SEVEN EMERALDS ALONE. ONE HUNDRED AND SEVENTY RUBIES. FORTY CARBUNCLES. TWO HUNDRED AND TEN SAPPHIRES. SIXTY-ONE AGATES, AND ONE HUNDRED AND FORTY-THREE DIAMONDS, INCLUDING THE GREAT MOGUL, THE SECOND LARGEST STONE IN EXISTENCE."

WE HID THE TREASURE IN THE FORT. I DREW FOUR PLANS, ONE FOR EACH OF US, AND PUT THE SIGN OF THE FOUR UPON THEM.

WHAT WE DIDN'T KNOW WAS THAT THE RAJAH HAD SENT A SECOND SERVANT TO SPY UPON THE FIRST. WHEN HE COULD FIND NO TRACE OF HIM, WORD WENT OUT AND THE BODY WAS SOON FOUND.

SO, YOU AND YOUR COMPANIONS WERE TRIED, FOUND GUILTY AND SENT AWAY FOR LIFE TO THE PENAL COLONY IN THE ANDAMAN ISLANDS?

BLAIR ISLAND... HOPE TOWN...

"IT WAS A DREARY, FEVER-STRICKEN PLACE, INFESTED WITH WILD CANNIBAL NATIVES."

"I LATER LANDED A BILLET IN THE DISPENSARY. FROM THERE, I COULD SEE ALL THE OFFICERS AND OFFICIALS AT THEIR DRINKING AND GAMBLING."

"MAJOR SHOLTO WAS THE HARDEST HIT. NIGHT AFTER NIGHT, HE GOT POORER AND POORER. ALL DAY HE'D WANDER ABOUT, MOOD AS BLACK AS THUNDER, DRINKING MORE THAN WAS GOOD FOR HIM."

"HE AND CAPTAIN MORSTAN WERE BOSOM FRIENDS, NEVER FAR APART. WHEN I HEARD THE MAJOR RAVING ABOUT HIS LOSSES, IT SET ME THINKING ON THE TREASURE."

"SO I DECIDED TO PUT A PROPOSAL TO THEM..."

ALL WE NEED IS A SMALL BOAT... SOME PROVISIONS, ENOUGH FOR MYSELF AND MY THREE COMPANIONS.

FOR THAT AND OUR FREEDOM, WE'LL GIVE YOU A FIFTH SHARE TO DIVIDE BETWEEN YOU.

A FIFTH! THAT'S NOT VERY TEMPTING! IF THERE WERE ONLY THE ONE OF YOU...

NO! IT IS NONE OR ALL. THE FOUR OF US HAVE SWORN IT!

WELL, WE ALL FINALLY AGREED TERMS — MYSELF, MY COMRADES, THE MAJOR AND THE CAPTAIN. WE SWORE THE MOST SOLEMN OATHS THAT MINDS COULD THINK AND LIPS UTTER.

I DREW UP CHARTS OF THE LOCATION OF THE TREASURE, SIGNED WITH THE SIGN OF THE FOUR...

BUT SHOLTO BETRAYED YOU ALL.

EVEN CAPTAIN MORSTAN COULD SEE THE VILLAINY OF IT. HE SWORE TO GO HOME AND SETTLE THE MATTER WITH HIM! SO HE WOULD... IF HE'D LIVED.

FROM THAT DAY, I LIVED ONLY FOR VENGEANCE. I THOUGHT OF IT BY DAY... I NURSED IT BY NIGHT.

TO HAVE MY HANDS AT SHOLTO'S THROAT WAS MY ONLY THOUGHT.

IT TOOK MANY WEARY YEARS, BUT ONE DAY, A LITTLE ANDAMAN ISLANDER WAS BROUGHT INTO THE DISPENSARY, SICK TO DEATH.

HE WAS AS VENOMOUS AS A YOUNG SNAKE, BUT I GOT HIM RIGHT.

AS A RESULT, HE BECAME VERY DEVOTED TO ME.

"THREE OR FOUR YEARS AGO, WE FOUND OURSELVES IN LONDON. I'D NO TROUBLE IN FINDING SHOLTO, BUT I NEEDED TO KNOW IF HE HAD REALISED THE TREASURE, OR IF HE STILL HAD IT."

I MADE FRIENDS WITH SOMEONE WHO'D HELP ME — I NAME NO NAMES, SO DON'T ASK — AND SOON FOUND THE MAJOR STILL HAD THE JEWELS, BUT WAS WELL GUARDED.

"WHEN I HEARD HE WAS DYING, I HURRIED TO THE HOUSE BUT ARRIVED TOO LATE. I PINNED THE SIGN OF THE FOUR TO HIS BOSOM, THAT HE SHOULD TAKE TO THE GRAVE A TOKEN FROM THE MEN HE'D ROBBED."

WHEN WORD CAME THE TREASURE HAD BEEN FOUND AT THE TOP OF THE HOUSE, I REASONED HOW TO REACH IT... WITH TONGA'S HELP.

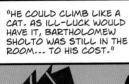

"HE COULD CLIMB LIKE A CAT. AS ILL-LUCK WOULD HAVE IT, BARTHOLOMEW SHOLTO WAS STILL IN THE ROOM... TO HIS COST."

"TONGA THOUGHT HE'D DONE SOMETHING CLEVER IN KILLING HIM. I FOUND HIM STRUTTING ABOUT AS PROUD AS A PEACOCK. HE WAS VERY MUCH SURPRISED WHEN I TOOK THE ROPE'S END TO HIM."

I TOOK THE TREASURE-BOX AND LEFT THE SIGN OF THE FOUR UPON THE TABLE TO SHOW IT HAD COME BACK TO THOSE WHO'D THE MOST RIGHT TO IT.

ALL THIS IS THE TRUTH. I'VE HELD NOTHING BACK.

I ONLY WISH THE WORLD TO KNOW HOW BADLY I HAVE BEEN SERVED BY MAJOR SHOLTO, AND HOW INNOCENT I AM OF THE DEATH OF HIS SON.

THE END

The HOUND of the BASKERVILLES

PREVIEW...

"THEY PASSED A NIGHT SHEPHERD UPON THE MOOR AND DEMANDED TO KNOW IF HE HAD SEEN THE HUNT."

"CURSING THE SHEPHERD, THE DRUNKEN SQUIRES RODE ON, BUT THEIR SKINS TURNED COLD AS THE BLACK MARE WENT PAST, TRAILING ITS BRIDLE AND EMPTY SADDLE."

"CRAZED WITH FEAR, HE SAID HE HAD SEEN THE MAIDEN WITH THE HOUNDS ON HER TRACK, HUGO BASKERVILLE ON HIS BLACK MARE, AND RUNNING MUTE BEHIND HIM A HOUND OF HELL AT HIS HEELS!"

"RIDING SLOWLY, THEY CAME UPON THE HOUNDS, WHIMPERING IN A CLUSTER, STARING EYES GAZING DOWN THE NARROW VALLEY BEFORE THEM."

"MORE SOBER THAN WHEN THEY STARTED, THREE OF THE BOLDEST RODE FORWARD INTO THE DEEP DIP OR GOYAL."

THE FACTS OF THE CASE ARE SIMPLE. BEFORE GOING TO BED, SIR CHARLES WAS IN THE HABIT OF TAKING A NOCTURNAL WALK DOWN BASKERVILLE HALL'S FAMOUS YEW ALLEY.

HE WAS TO START FOR LONDON THE NEXT DAY AND ORDERED BARRYMORE TO PREPARE HIS LUGGAGE.

"AT MIDNIGHT, BARRYMORE, FINDING THE HALL DOOR STILL OPEN, BECAME ALARMED AND WENT IN SEARCH OF HIS MASTER."

"THE DAY HAD BEEN WET AND SIR CHARLES' FOOTPRINTS WERE EASILY TRACED DOWN THE ALLEY. HALFWAY ALONG IS A GATE THAT LEADS OUT ONTO THE MOOR."

"SIR CHARLES HAD EVIDENTLY STOOD THERE FOR SOME TIME BEFORE PROCEEDING DOWN TO THE FAR END OF THE ALLEY WHERE HIS BODY WAS DISCOVERED."

Follow the world's only consulting detective...

ISBN 978-1-910593-33-2

ISBN 978-1-910593-35-6

SHERLOCK HOLMES

ISBN 978-1-910593-32-5

ISBN 978-1-910593-34-9

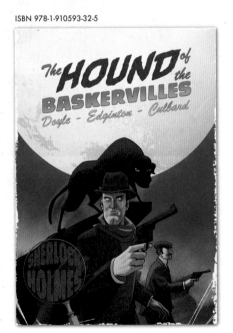

...on four deadly adventures.